Maths Weekly Workout
Year 6

Peter Patilla &
Paul Broadbent

First published 2001

Letts Educational
The Chiswick Centre
414 Chiswick High Rd
London
W4 5TF
Tel: (020) 8996 3333
Fax: (020) 8742 8390

www.letts-education.com

Text © Peter Patilla and Paul Broadbent
Illustrations © Peter and Janet Simmonett
Cover illustration © Peter and Janet Simmonett
Editorial, design and production by Gecko Limited, Cambridge

British Library Cataloguing-in-Publication Data
A CIP record for this book is available from the British Library.

ISBN 1 84085 623 8

Printed and bound in the UK.
Letts Educational, a division of Granada Learning Ltd.
Part of Granada Media Group.

CONTENTS

Solving problems: how to use this book

Share your ideas with your partner and listen to their ideas.

Write out your rough workings very neatly.

It is your problem. Try not to ask the teacher for help.

After each problem set yourself a challenge.

These are problems so do not give up right away if you become stuck.

Why not make a maths log book that keeps all your problems together?

Why not make a group or class notice-board to show your results?

Why not check your answers with your partner?

Why not write results on Post-it notes? They can be moved and rearranged.

Why not try to find lots of different solutions to each problem?

Why not make a poster to show your results?

Think about working on the problem at home.

Cross over

This is a game for two players.

Each player needs a calculator.

To play

- Each player chooses a different number to put on their display.

- The player with the smaller number always adds.
  The player with the larger number always subtracts.

- Take turns to add or subtract any number from the display, so that the two numbers get closer and closer.

- The aim is **not** to cross over the other player's display number.

Example

Player A	Player B
17	36
+8 → 25	−7 → 29
+3 → 28	−0.6 → 28.4
+0.25 → <u>28.25</u>	−0.2 → <u>28.2</u>

Player A wins because 28.2 'crosses over' and is less than 28.25.

Try giving points and keep score over a number of rounds.

Use decimal numbers to help keep the numbers from 'crossing over'.

Digital root patterns

Digital roots are found by adding together the digits of a number.

52 5 + 2 ⟩ 7 I stage

49 4 + 9 ⟩ 13 I + 3 ⟩ 4 2 stages

These are the digital roots for the ×5 table.

$1 \times 5 = 5 \rightarrow 5$

$2 \times 5 = 10 \rightarrow 1$

$3 \times 5 = 15 \rightarrow 6$

$4 \times 5 = 20 \rightarrow 2$

$5 \times 5 = 25 \rightarrow 7$

$6 \times 5 = 30 \rightarrow 3$

$7 \times 5 = 35 \rightarrow 8$

$8 \times 5 = 40 \rightarrow 4$

$9 \times 5 = 45 \rightarrow 9$

$10 \times 5 = 50 \rightarrow 5$

Draw a digital root pattern for the ×5 table like this.

Start at 5, and draw a line to 1, then 6, 2, 7, …

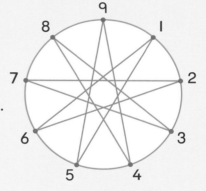

Trace this circle for the positions of the 9 dots.

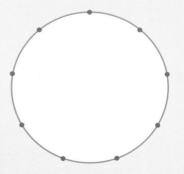

Investigate digital root patterns for other multiplication tables.

7

Multiplication patterns

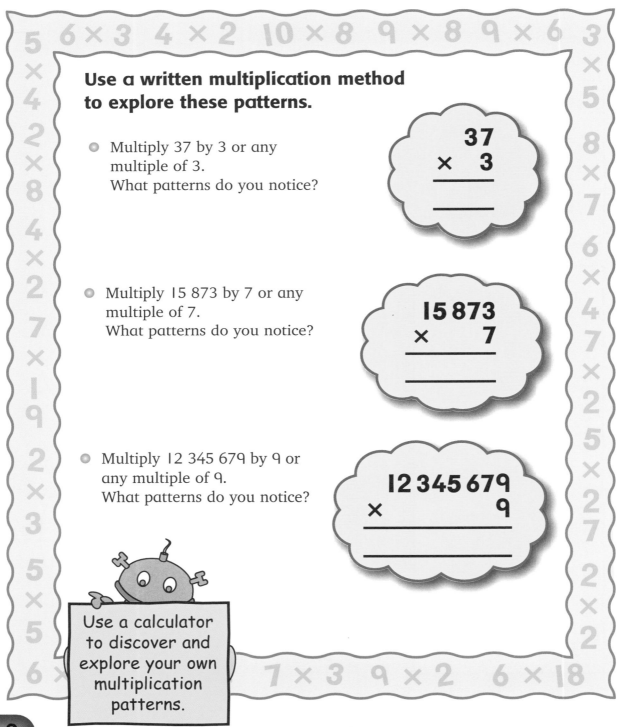

Use a written multiplication method to explore these patterns.

- Multiply 37 by 3 or any multiple of 3.
  What patterns do you notice?

$$\begin{array}{r} 37 \\ \times \quad 3 \\ \hline \end{array}$$

- Multiply 15 873 by 7 or any multiple of 7.
  What patterns do you notice?

$$\begin{array}{r} 15\,873 \\ \times \quad 7 \\ \hline \end{array}$$

- Multiply 12 345 679 by 9 or any multiple of 9.
  What patterns do you notice?

$$\begin{array}{r} 12\,345\,679 \\ \times \quad 9 \\ \hline \end{array}$$

Use a calculator to discover and explore your own multiplication patterns.

8

Decimal triangles

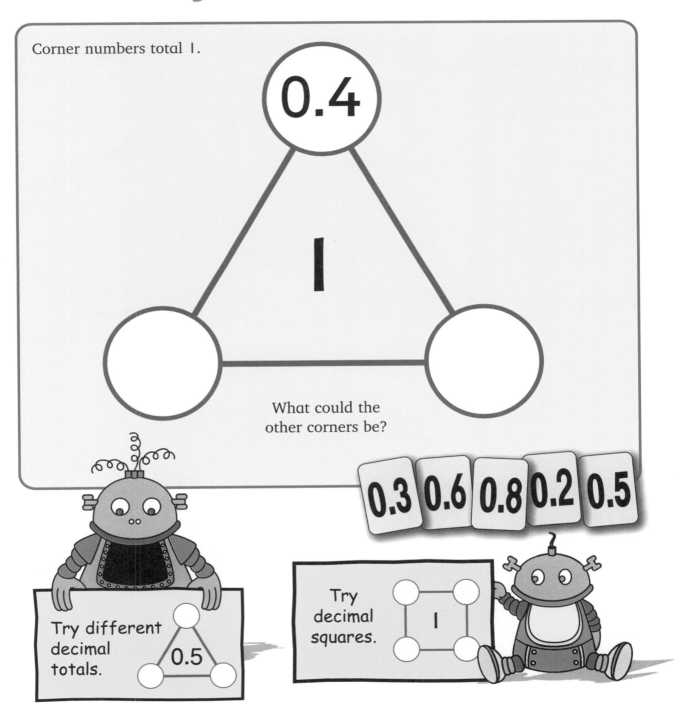

Corner numbers total 1.

0.4

1

What could the other corners be?

0.3 0.6 0.8 0.2 0.5

Try different decimal totals.

0.5

Try decimal squares.

1

Missing percentages

Choose one of these.

What could the missing numbers be?

 % of = 20p

 % of = £5

Record your results. How many different examples can you make?

Try different amounts of money.

UNIT 6

Graph stories

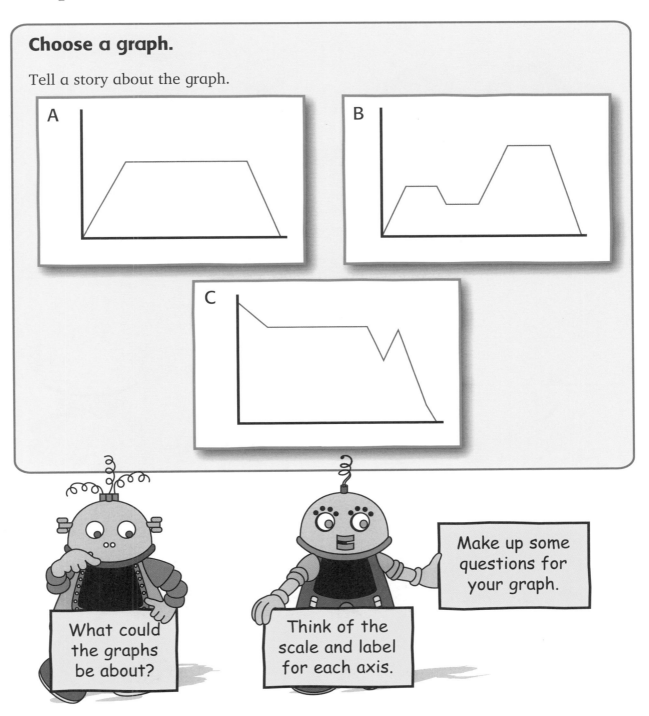

Choose a graph.

Tell a story about the graph.

A

B

C

What could the graphs be about?

Think of the scale and label for each axis.

Make up some questions for your graph.

11

Frogs

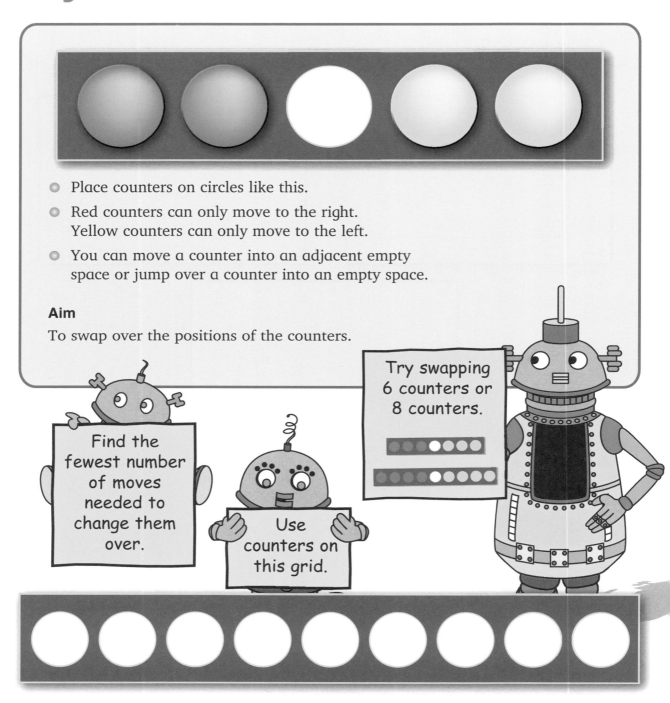

- Place counters on circles like this.
- Red counters can only move to the right.
  Yellow counters can only move to the left.
- You can move a counter into an adjacent empty
  space or jump over a counter into an empty space.

Aim

To swap over the positions of the counters.

Try swapping
6 counters or
8 counters.

Find the
fewest number
of moves
needed to
change them
over.

Use
counters on
this grid.

Polyiamonds

Polyiamonds are made by joining equilateral triangles.

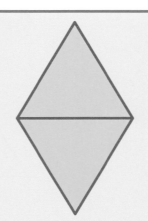

2 triangles make a **diamond**.

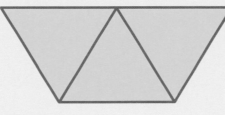

3 triangles make a **triamond**.

Find some more triamonds.

4 triangles make a **tetriamond**.

Find some more tetriamonds.

Try to find all the different shapes you can make.

Explore all the different **pentiamonds** that you can make.

13

Perimeter chains

Look at these triangle chains.

A

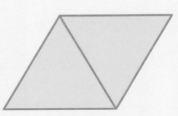

I unit   I unit

I unit

B

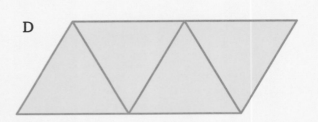

C

D

This table shows the perimeter of each shape.

Shape	Perimeter
A	3
B	4
C	5
D	6

Explore the perimeters of other shape chains.

Look for patterns in your tables of results.

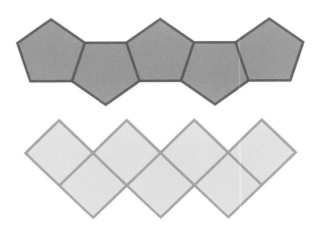

Heavier or lighter?

Play this game in pairs.

You need

- a variety of objects to weigh
- weighing scales

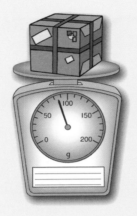

To play

- Player A holds an object and estimates its weight to the nearest gram.
- Player B then says whether they think the object is **heavier** or **lighter** than the estimate.
- Weigh the object. If player B is correct, they get 2 points. If they are wrong, player A gets 2 points.
- Take turns to estimate weights of objects.

Decide whether to weigh to the nearest gram or the nearest 10 grams.

Keep a score – the first to 10 points is the winner.

15

Palindromes

The 10th of February 2001 was a special date.

When it is written out it is a **palindrome**: **10:02:2001**
A **palindromic number** reads the same
backwards as forwards.

○ Choose any number.

Reverse the digits and add.

717 is palindromic.

$$\begin{array}{r} 314 \\ +\ 413 \\ \hline 717 \end{array}$$

○ Try another number.

Reverse and add.

$$\begin{array}{r} 154 \\ +\ 451 \\ \hline 605 \end{array}$$

605 is not palindromic.

Reverse and try again.

1111 is palindromic.

$$\begin{array}{r} 605 \\ +\ 506 \\ \hline 1111 \end{array}$$

Are palindromic numbers always multiples of 11?

Investigate other numbers. Do they always end up as palindromes? How many steps do they take?

Happy numbers

32 is a happy number!

This is how to work out if a number is happy.

3^2 2^2

$9 + 4 =$ **13**

1^2 3^2

$1 + 9 =$ **10**

If you end with a 1, the number you started with is happy.

1^2 0^2

$1 + 0 =$ **1**

Is 16 happy? What about 9?

10, 13 and 32 are all happy numbers. Which numbers to 50 are also happy?

Display your results and choose a way to group them. Are there any patterns to help find happy numbers?

17

Grid pictures

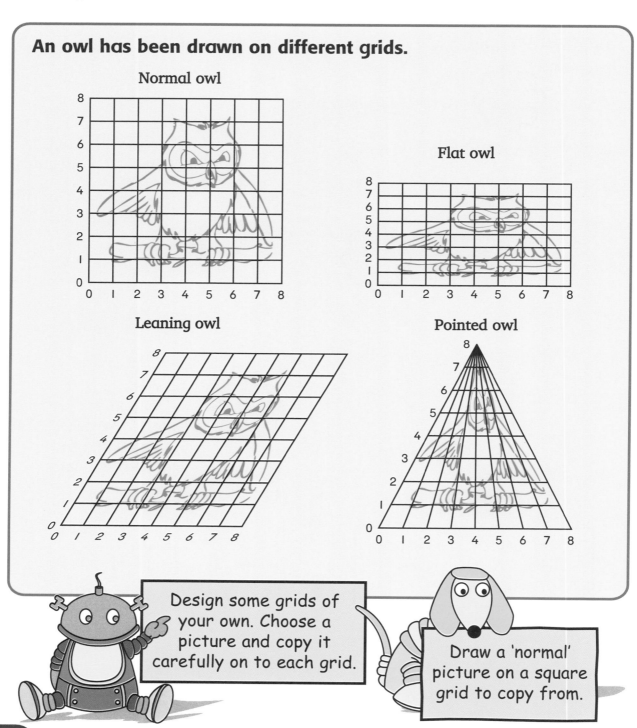

An owl has been drawn on different grids.

Normal owl

Flat owl

Leaning owl

Pointed owl

Design some grids of your own. Choose a picture and copy it carefully on to each grid.

Draw a 'normal' picture on a square grid to copy from.

18

Dice chains

Copy this number chain.

Choose your own signs to put in it.
Here is an example.

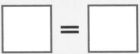

- Roll a pair of dice twice, to get four numbers.
- Put the numbers in any four boxes you choose.
- Write numbers in the other boxes so that the chain is correct.

Check the chain with a calculator.

Try to get a negative number answer.

Give yourself a target answer. Roll the pair of dice twice and write the numbers in any of the boxes. Try to make the target answer.

19

Cross-numbers

Write clues for this cross-number.
Use × and – only.

Across	Down
1	1
2	2
4	3
5	6
7	7
8	8
9	9
10	

¹3	8		²1	2	³2
1		⁴2	4		0
⁵6	⁶4			⁷1	3
	0			0	
⁸7	0		⁹1	2	5
4		¹⁰4	8		

> You can use brackets:
> (7 × 6) – 4 = 38

Write in answers and make up clues for this cross-number. You can only use ÷ and + for the clues.

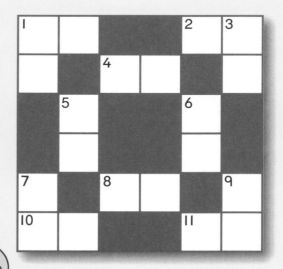

Russian multiplication

This is a multiplication method used many years ago in Russia. It involves halving and doubling.

Follow the method for 45 × 28.

Step 1

Halve the left-hand column. Ignore any remainders and stop at 1.

Double the right-hand column.

45	×	28
22		56
11		112
5		224
2		448
1		896

Step 2

Cross out all the even numbers in the left-hand column and the corresponding numbers in the right-hand column.

Step 3

Add the numbers that remain in the right-hand column.

45	×	28
~~22~~		~~56~~
11		112
5		224
~~2~~		~~448~~
1		896
		1260

Try this method with some of your own long multiplications.

Time yourself. Is this a quick method compared with others you use?

21

Cities in the USA

Look at these.

A	$1
B	$2
C	$3
D	$4
E	$5
F	$6
G	$7
H	$8
I	$9
J	$10
K	$11
L	$12
M	$13
N	$14
O	$15
P	$16
Q	$17
R	$18
S	$19
T	$20
U	$21
V	$22
W	$23
X	$24
Y	$25
Z	$26

Using these prices, NEW YORK is worth $111.

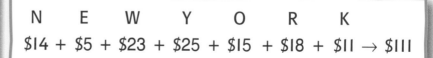

N   E   W   Y   O   R   K

$14 + $5 + $23 + $25 + $15 + $18 + $11 → $111

Which is the most valuable city in the USA?

Which city in the USA is worth the least?

Are there any cities that are worth multiples of $10 or $100?

Fraction patterns

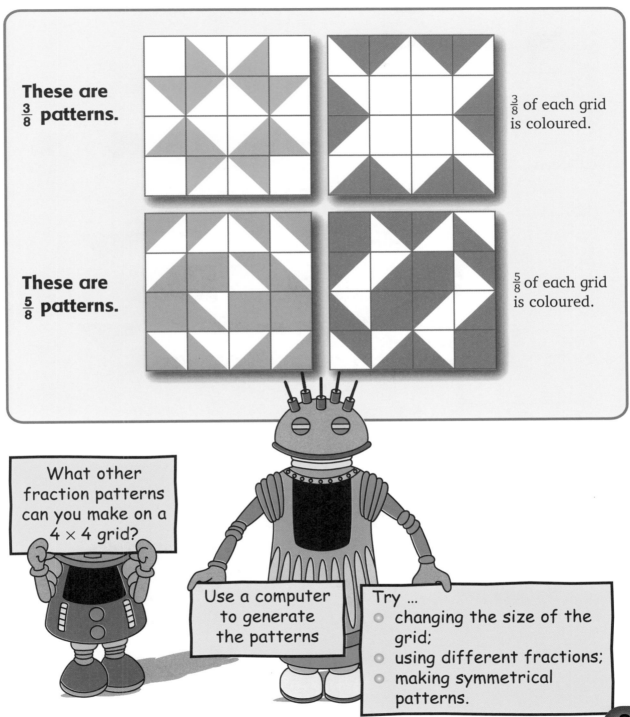

These are $\frac{3}{8}$ patterns.

$\frac{3}{8}$ of each grid is coloured.

These are $\frac{5}{8}$ patterns.

$\frac{5}{8}$ of each grid is coloured.

What other fraction patterns can you make on a 4 × 4 grid?

Use a computer to generate the patterns

Try …
- changing the size of the grid;
- using different fractions;
- making symmetrical patterns.

Friezes

This simple tile can be used to make friezes.

Translate

Reflect

Rotate

Design your own tile and make different friezes.

Try using a computer to translate, reflect and rotate a tile.

Swap over

This is a puzzle for one player.

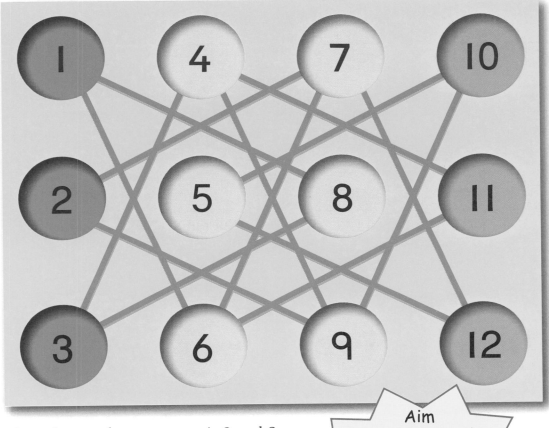

- Place three red counters on 1, 2 and 3.
- Place three blue counters on 10, 11 and 12.
- Slide the counters along the lines.
- Only one counter can be at any circle and no jumping is allowed.
- Counters can move forwards and backwards and in any order.

Aim
To swap over the positions of the red and blue counters.

Make up a game that uses the puzzle board.

Keep a running total of the numbers you land on. What is the lowest total you can make?

Tessellating tiles

Make a tessellating tile from an equilateral triangle, like this.

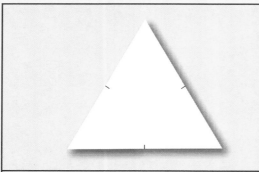

I Cut out an equilateral triangle and mark the mid-points of the sides.

2 Cut out sections of the triangle from a corner to a mid-point of each side.

3 Stick the pieces to the other sides of the triangle.

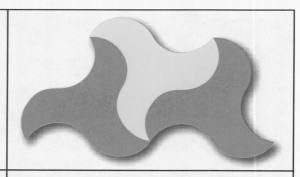

4 Draw round the shape tile to make a tessellated pattern.

Try different cut-out shapes.

26

Time graphs

Here are two graphs with missing labels.

- What could the graphs be about?
- What could the missing labels be?

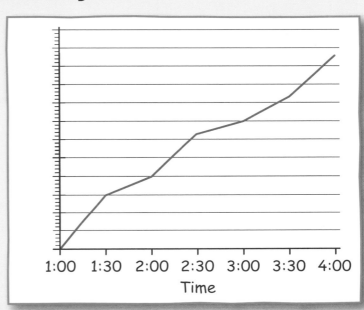

Make up some questions to ask about the graphs.

Compare the information from the two graphs.

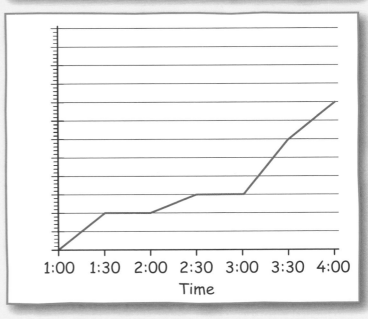

Decimal digits

The digits 1, 2 and 3 are missing.

Write the completed calculations.

$$
\begin{array}{r}
4\square.\square5 \\
+ \ 50.9\square \\
\hline
94.07
\end{array}
\qquad
\begin{array}{r}
84.0\square \\
- \ \square9.\square5 \\
\hline
44.76
\end{array}
$$

Choose one of these calculations to complete.

- Choose from the digits 0–9. Each digit can be used once only.

- Make answers as close as possible to 55.55.

$$
\begin{array}{r}
\square\square.\square\square \\
+ \ \square\square.\square\square \\
\hline
\end{array}
\qquad
\begin{array}{r}
\square\square.\square\square \\
- \ \square\square.\square\square \\
\hline
\end{array}
$$

What if you could use each digit more than once?

Try changing the answer to 22.22.

Abacus numbers

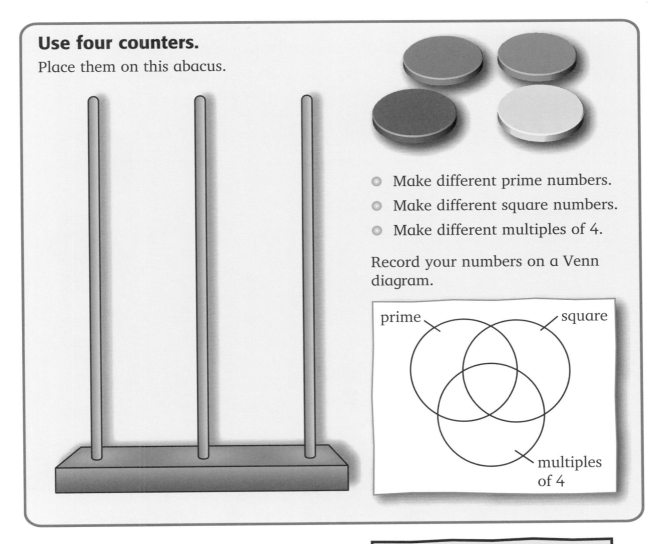

Use four counters.

Place them on this abacus.

- Make different prime numbers.
- Make different square numbers.
- Make different multiples of 4.

Record your numbers on a Venn diagram.

prime · square

multiples of 4

Which square numbers can you make with ...
- 1 counter?
- 2 counters?
- 3 counters?

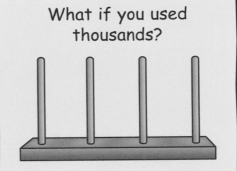

What if you used thousands?

29

Shape words

A	
B	
C	
D	
E	
F	
G	
H	
I	
J	
K	
L	
M	
N	
O	
P	
Q	
R	
S	
T	
U	
V	
W	
X	
Y	
Z	

Make an alphabet list.

Collect shape words to go with each letter of the alphabet.

Which letter has the most words?

Which letters have no words?

Product walls

This is a product wall.

76 800

320   240

8   40   6

Try to work out the missing numbers.

13 500

30

Make up your own product wall puzzles.

Give your puzzles to others, with just the centre numbers written in.

Target numbers

Play this game in pairs or small groups.

- Shuffle 1–20 number cards and deal five cards to each player.

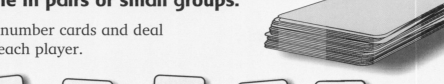

10 14 1 9 15

- Use the cards with +, −, ×, ÷ and brackets. The target number is **750**.

- The winner is the closest to the target.

$$14 - 9 = 5$$
$$5 \times 15 = 75$$
$$75 \times 10 = 750$$
$$750 \div 1 = 750$$

2 5 8 20 6 12 4 16 7 19 8 17 11 18 13 3

Try setting a time limit, say 2 minutes.

Try changing the target number.

Try adding the rule that all five number cards must be used.

Number mobiles

Here is a number mobile.

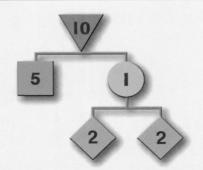

On each of these mobiles, if the shape is the same, then so is the number.

Each side of the mobile must balance.

Choose a mobile and find ways of balancing when 10 is in the triangle. Remember, you can use decimals.

Try the same thing with the other mobiles.

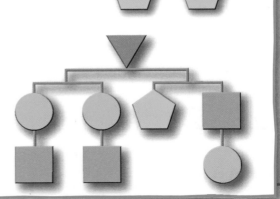

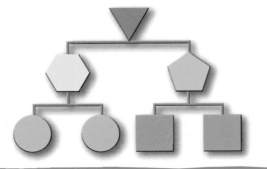

What if the number in the triangle was 1?

Design your own number mobile for 10, ignoring the shapes but keeping it balanced.

Place the digits

This is a game to play on your own or as a group.

Choose to play game A or game B.

- Shuffle a set of 0–9 digit cards and place them face down in a pile.
- Turn over the top card and place it on the grid in any position you want.
- Continue this, turning over 6 cards and placing them one at a time on the grid.
- Check your numbers. Is the result true?

Try making up your own game grids.

Game A

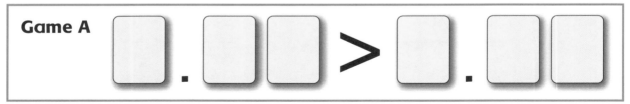

Game B

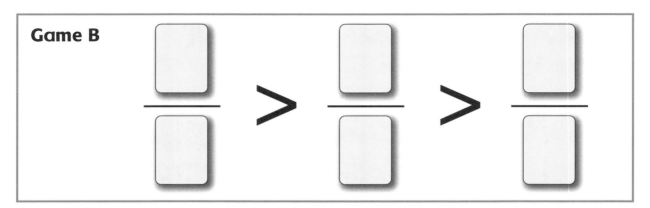

Two-colour models

Make models from interlocking cubes.

Use 2 blue cubes for every 3 yellow cubes.

Explore different 20-cube models.

Sort the models.

- Which are cuboids?
- Which are symmetrical models?
- Which have the most faces?

What if the models have more than 20 cubes?

Pie charts

Choose one of these pie charts.

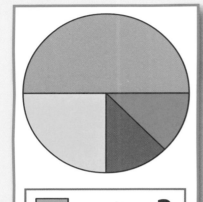

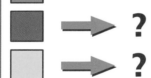

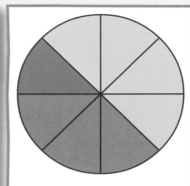
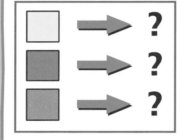

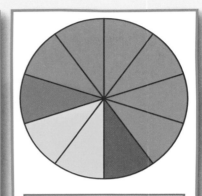
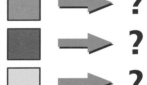

- What could your pie chart be about?
- What are the sectors?
- Write some questions about your pie chart.

Work out the number for each sector and the total.

Ask questions involving fractions as well as whole numbers.

Cops and robbers

This is a game for two players.

Choose whether to be the cop or the robber.

How to play

- Place a blue counter on the cop.
  Place a red counter on the robber.

- The cop moves first, along any path to the next building.

- Take turns to move along a path.

- Buildings can be visited more than once.

- The cop must catch the robber in fewer than 7 moves.

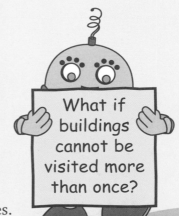

What if buildings cannot be visited more than once?

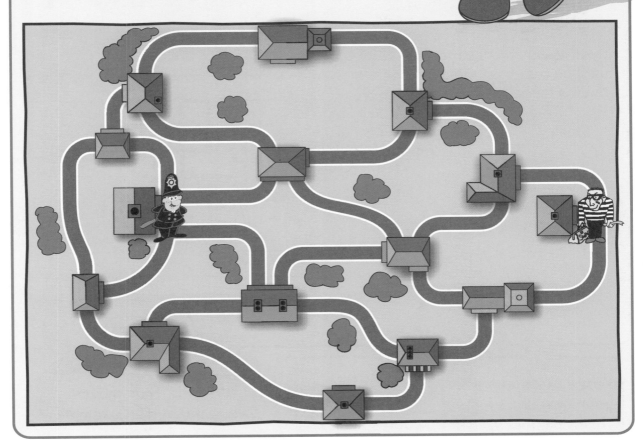

Snail spirals

Cyril the snail only travels along lines and always turns clockwise through 90°.

This is his snail trail for (1, 3, 2).

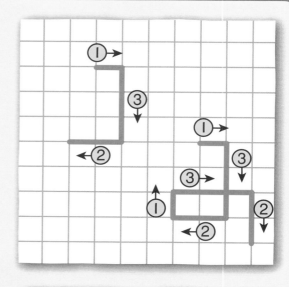

Cyril repeats the instructions until he comes off the grid or returns to the starting point.

This is his finished spiral.

Try this snail spiral on squared paper.

(2, 4, 2)

Why not choose your own set of three numbers?

Can you find a way to sort your spirals?

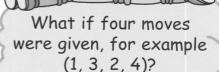

What if four moves were given, for example (1, 3, 2, 4)?

Big names

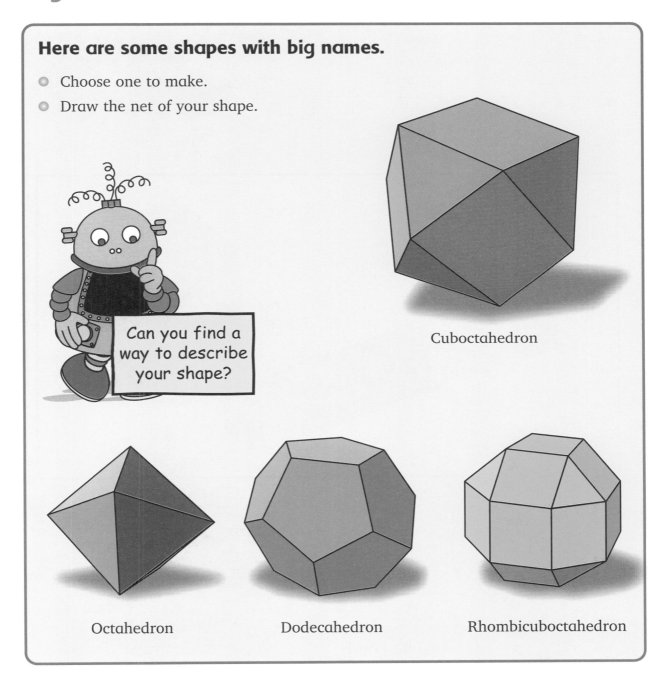

Here are some shapes with big names.

- Choose one to make.
- Draw the net of your shape.

Can you find a way to describe your shape?

Cuboctahedron

Octahedron

Dodecahedron

Rhombicuboctahedron

Surface area

- Make different models, each with a volume of 8 cube units.
- What is the surface area of each model?

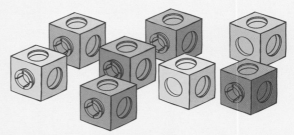

Surface area = 24 square units

Surface area = 34 square units

These are the largest and smallest areas.

Can you sort your models?

Can you have a surface area with an odd number of units?

Try using 12 cubes. Which surface areas can you make?

40

Calculator target

- Find other ways of making 0.1 with 8 key touches.
- Use +, −, × or ÷ to calculate.

- Which keys could have been touched?
- Find different solutions.

Try grouping your solutions by calculation: +, −, ×, ÷

Set a different decimal target number.

Change the number of touches.

Dotty primes

These 'dotty primes' have been made on 5 × 3 grids.

Using **7** counters

Using **11** counters

Prime numbers have been used to make symmetrical patterns.

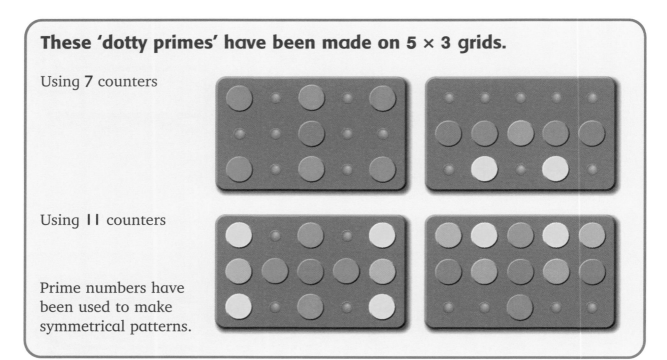

Make your own 'dotty prime' patterns by placing counters on this grid.

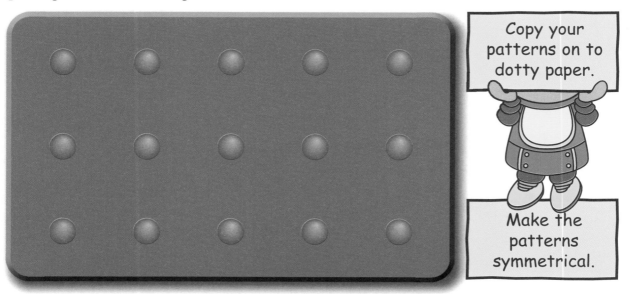

Copy your patterns on to dotty paper.

Make the patterns symmetrical.

Eggs and birds

You need a ruler, compasses, scissors and thin card.

- Measure this diagram to the nearest mm.
- Copy the egg pattern as accurately as you can on to thin card.
- Cut along the **black** lines to get 9 pieces.
- Use these pieces as a template for paper shapes.

Arrange the pieces to make bird shapes.

Make 3

A game for two players

You need a set of counters.

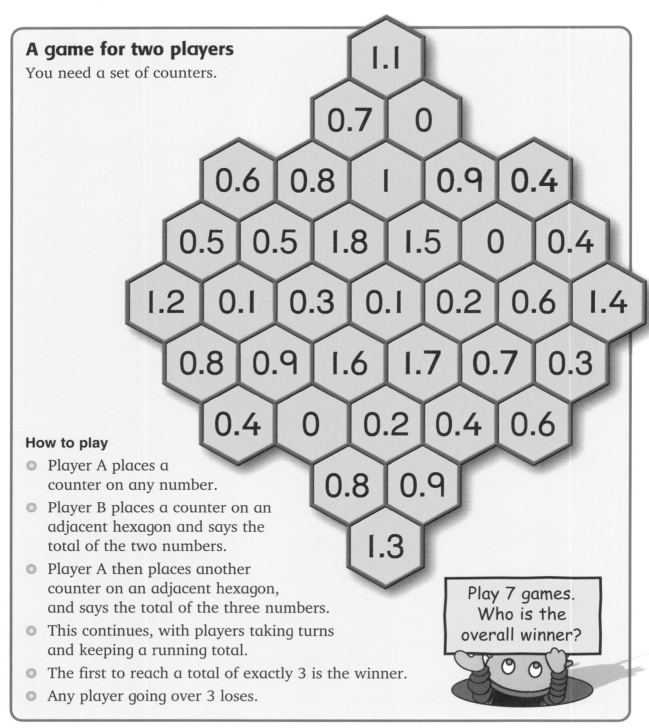

How to play

- Player A places a counter on any number.
- Player B places a counter on an adjacent hexagon and says the total of the two numbers.
- Player A then places another counter on an adjacent hexagon, and says the total of the three numbers.
- This continues, with players taking turns and keeping a running total.
- The first to reach a total of exactly 3 is the winner.
- Any player going over 3 loses.

Play 7 games. Who is the overall winner?

Anytime puzzle

Stick shapes

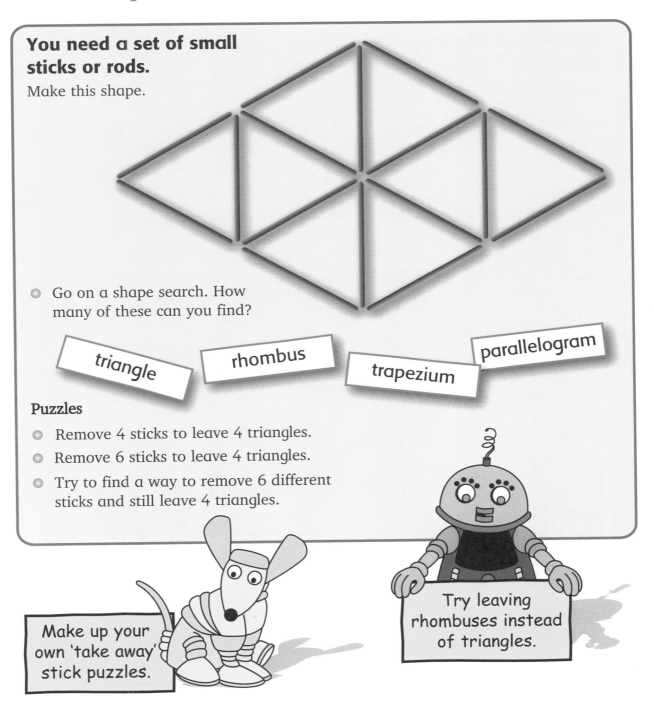

You need a set of small sticks or rods.

Make this shape.

- Go on a shape search. How many of these can you find?

triangle   rhombus   trapezium   parallelogram

Puzzles

- Remove 4 sticks to leave 4 triangles.
- Remove 6 sticks to leave 4 triangles.
- Try to find a way to remove 6 different sticks and still leave 4 triangles.

Make up your own 'take away' stick puzzles.

Try leaving rhombuses instead of triangles.

Super squares

A game for two players

You need: square dotty paper and a different coloured pen for each player.

How to play

- Copy this number grid on square dotty paper or squared paper.

- Player A starts by joining two adjacent dots, horizontally or vertically.

- Player B uses a different colour to join two different dots, anywhere on the grid.

- This continues until a line is drawn to complete a square. Whoever drew the last line colours in the square.
$$-6$$

- When all the squares are completed, the numbers for each player's colour are totalled. The winner is the player with the highest total.

1	5	−3	8	0
−6	2	4	−7	−3
−2	−1	9	2	4
6	0	−5	−6	−3
−8	3	−4	7	−9

Anytime puzzle

Glossary

Adjacent

This means 'lying next to'.

5 and 6 are adjacent whole numbers.

7 and 9 are adjacent odd numbers.

Equilateral triangle

This is a triangle with each side the same length and each angle 60°.

Factors

A factor is a number that divides exactly into another number. Each number apart from 1 has at least two factors: 1 and itself. A number can have several factors. The factors of 10 are 1, 2, 5 and 10.

Multiples

Multiples are like the answers to times tables. Multiples of 4 are 4, 8, 12, 16, ... Multiples do not stop at the tenth one, they go on and on.

Net

This is a flat or 2-D shape which will fold up to make a 3-D shape.

The net of a cube is made from six connecting squares.

Per cent

A percentage is a special type of fraction out of 100.

30% is $\frac{30}{100}$, or 30 parts out of 100.

10% of 40 is 4.

50% of £6 is £3.

Perimeter

This is the distance measured around the edge of an object.

Prime number

This is a special number that only has two factors, 1 and itself. In other words it cannot be divided exactly by any number, apart from 1 and itself.

7 is a prime number because it can only be divided by 1 and 7.

23 is a prime number as it can only be divided by 1 and 23.

1 is not a prime number since it only has one factor.

Product

This is the answer to a multiplication.

The product of 3 and 7 is 21.

Square number

To square a number is to multiply it by itself.

The square of 4 is 4 × 4 which is 16. So 16 is a square number.

The first five square numbers are 1, 4, 9, 16 and 25. They are called square numbers because they can be shown as a square pattern of dots.

Symmetrical

A shape or pattern is symmetrical when it can be divided into two parts that reflect each other exactly. This is called line or mirror symmetry.

Tessellation

A tessellating pattern is made by fitting shapes together without leaving gaps and without overlapping.

Maths content

Term 1

Week 1	Unit 1	Decimal numbers
Week 2	Unit 2	Multiplication facts
Week 3	Unit 3	Written multiplication
Week 4	Unit 4	Totalling decimals
Week 5	Unit 5	Percentages
Week 6	Unit 6	Line graphs
Week 7	Unit 7	Strategy puzzle
Week 8	Unit 8	Exploring shapes
Week 9	Unit 9	Perimeters of shapes
Week 10	Unit 10	Estimating and weighing objects
Week 11	Unit 11	Calculation problems
Week 12	Unit 12	Number patterns
Week 13	Unit 13	Shape and grid references

Term 2

Week 1	Unit 14	Calculation
Week 2	Unit 15	Calculation
Week 3	Unit 16	Long multiplication
Week 4	Unit 17	Money calculation
Week 5	Unit 18	Fractions of shapes
Week 6	Unit 19	Transformation geometry
Week 7	Unit 20	Logic puzzle
Week 8	Unit 21	Shape and area
Week 9	Unit 22	Line graphs
Week 10	Unit 23	Calculation problems
Week 11	Unit 24	Properties of number
Week 12	Unit 25	Shape vocabulary

Term 3

Week 1	Unit 26	Multiplying with large numbers
Week 2	Unit 27	Calculation
Week 3	Unit 28	Number facts
Week 4	Unit 29	Comparing fractions and decimals
Week 5	Unit 30	Ratio
Week 6	Unit 31	Interpreting pie charts
Week 7	Unit 32	Logic puzzle
Week 8	Unit 33	Shape investigation
Week 9	Unit 34	3-D shapes
Week 10	Unit 35	Area and volume
Week 11	Unit 36	Calculating with decimals
Week 12	Unit 37	Patterns and arrangements
Week 13	Unit 38	Exploring shapes

Anytime puzzles

Unit 39	Decimal addition
Unit 40	Shape puzzle
Unit 41	Negative number game